Radiant
Heart

bendon®

Ashland, OH 44805
bendonpub.com
1-888-5-BENDON

Elsa was the older sister. Anna was the younger sister.
They loved to play together.

One night, Elsa created a magical winter wonderland–
in the Great Hall!

Anna and Elsa went sliding on ice, had a snowball
fight, and built a snowman.

© Disney

Then, one of Elsa's magic ice blasts hit Anna by accident. It made Anna so cold.

© Disney

The king and queen rushed the girls to the trolls,
whose magic could help Anna.

The trolls did help Anna but said Elsa's magic could grow to be dangerous. The king made Elsa wear gloves.

The king put walls up all around the Arendelle castle.
The girls weren't allowed to leave.

After that, Elsa wouldn't play with Anna anymore
because she was afraid of hurting her.

© Disney

The sisters have grown up, and now it is time for Elsa
to become queen.

Kristoff is an ice harvester. He's going to sell ice to the people below on this warm coronation day.

Prince Hans has sailed to Arendelle from afar.

Elsa manages to hold the royal scepter and orb
without freezing them. Just barely!

Elsa is crowned Queen of Arendelle.

Anna dances with the handsome Prince Hans, then they talk about everything.

Anna is sure this is true love. She says yes when
Prince Hans asks her to marry him!

Anna tells Elsa that she and Prince Hans are engaged.
Elsa thinks it's too soon.

Elsa won't allow Anna to marry Hans. Anna pulls off
Elsa's glove to get her attention.

Elsa loses control when Anna asks her what she's so afraid of. Elsa blasts ice in front of all her guests.

© Disney

Everyone is shocked by Elsa's display of icy magic.

Elsa is afraid. She runs away across the fjords,
the water freezing under her feet.

© Disney

Anna must go after her sister. She asks Hans to take
care of the kingdom while she's away.

The farther Elsa gets from Arendelle, the freer she is
to use her powers.

© Disney

Elsa builds a magnificent ice palace on
the North Mountain.

Elsa changes her hair and dress.
She becomes the Snow Queen!

Anna must find her sister.

Anna meets Kristoff, who's covered in snow. He knows
where the storm is coming from.

Kristoff is an expert mountain man,
as well as an ice harvester.

Kristoff's best friend is a reindeer named Sven.

Anna would like Kristoff to take her up
the North Mountain to find Elsa.

Kristoff agrees to help Anna find her sister.
They have a lot to talk about!

Anna, Kristoff, and Sven meet a snowman named
Olaf in Elsa's icy wonderland.

Olaf is a magical snowman who likes warm hugs.

Anna is determined to get to her sister, even if that means climbing a sheer wall of ice!

Olaf leads Anna and Kristoff to Elsa's
magnificent ice palace.

Anna begs Elsa to return home. Elsa can't go back;
it's too dangerous for everyone involved.

Elsa knows she can never be close to Anna.
She's afraid of hurting her again—then she does!

Anna's hurt, but she's still worried about Elsa
and won't leave.

Elsa makes a giant snowman named Marshmallow
to escort her guests off the mountain.

Marshmallow chases Anna and Kristoff
to the mountain's edge.

Anna, Kristoff, and Olaf escape Marshmallow, but now
Anna's hair is turning white.

© Disney

Anna's horse returns to Arendelle without her.

Hans heads off to find Anna.

Kristoff takes Anna to his friends. The trolls' magic
could help her.

The old troll is very worried. Only an act of true love will save Anna from freezing solid.

Maybe a true love's kiss from Hans will save Anna.
Kristoff and Sven rush her to Arendelle.

Kristoff delivers Anna to the castle gate, where the
royal staff pull her inside. It's hard to say good-bye.

© Disney

Anna explains everything to Hans and asks him
to kiss her. He refuses.

Hans reveals his evil plan to take over the kingdom,
then puts out the fire.

© Disney

Anna doesn't have the strength to warn her sister
about Hans. She's so very cold.

Sven wants Kristoff to return to Arendelle
to be with Anna.

Olaf arrives to help Anna. He spies Kristoff returning
to Arendelle. Kristoff must love Anna!

Kissing Kristoff is Anna's only hope. She follows
Olaf out of the castle window.

Anna has little time left. She must reach Kristoff!

Anna finds Kristoff, and she starts to run to him.

© Disney

Hans is creeping up behind Elsa, sword in hand.

Hans is going to hurt Elsa! Anna jumps in front of his
sword, just as she freezes solid.

Hans's sword breaks, but he's still willing to use it to
hurt the sisters. Kristoff will stop him.

© Disney

Elsa can't believe Anna froze solid.
But then Anna starts to thaw!

Anna's act of true love in saving her sister has melted
Anna's frozen heart.

Anna has taught Elsa about love and not being afraid.
Elsa can now control her magic,
so she brings back summer.

Kristoff, Anna, Elsa, and even Olaf
–with his protective cloud–are glad that
summer has returned to Arendelle.

Anna is thankful to Kristoff for his help in saving
her sister and her kingdom.

Finally, Anna and Elsa can play together again.